I SPY PHONICS FUN

Learning Letters K and L

In this book you'll see letters printed in red. These are *I Spy Phonics Fun* learning letters. Learning the sounds of these letters will help you read.

The learning letter "k" sounds like the "k" in "key." Sometimes the letters "c" and "k" come together to sound like the "k" in "chick."

The learning letter "l" sounds like the "l" in "lion."

I Spy Sight Words

You will see the following words in this book. The rhythm, rhyme, and repetition of the I Spy riddles will help you learn them.

I	spy	a
an	that	for
the	on	and

I Spy Challenge Words

When you come to these words, the I Spy pictures will help you remember them.

surfer's	yellow	bear	hair
train	dusty	pig	golden

I spy

a king,

a surfer's hair,

a pink fish,

and a koala bear.

I spy

a skeleton,

a golden key,

a track for a train,

and a yellow golf tee.

I spy

 an airplane,

a yellow sail,

 a watermelon,

and a lobster's tail.

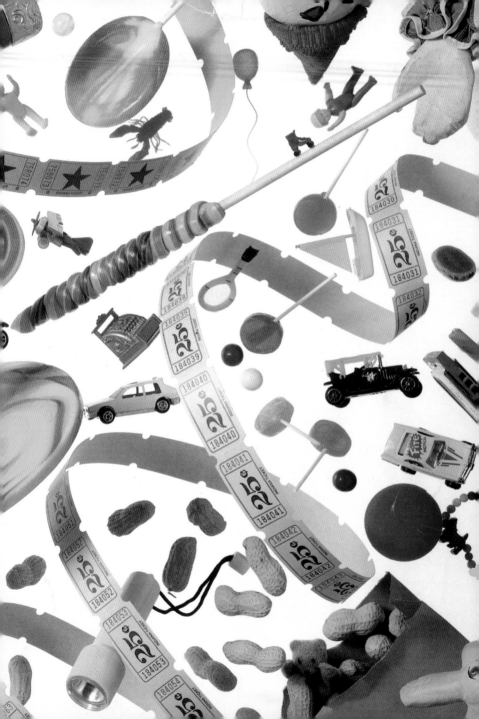

I spy

a lamp,

a dusty old clock,

a pair of glasses,

and a pig on a block.

I spy these L words
somewhere else in this book.

lobster's tail

watermelon

lamp

airplane

I spy these K words
somewhere else in this book.

block

kangaroo

key

pink

I spy two words that end with the letter L. Do they rhyme?

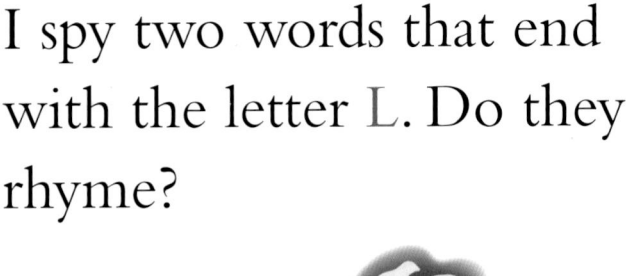

pail

tail

jack

I spy two words that start
with the letter L.

string

lion

leaf

I spy two words that end
with the letters CK.
Do they rhyme?

chick

jelly bean

lipstick

I spy two words that start with the letter K.

kitten

jewels

king

I spy two words that start with the letter K.

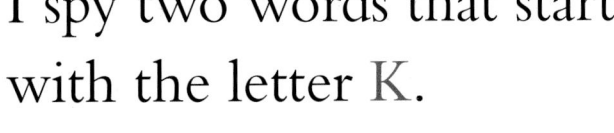

kite

insect

kangaroo